héng	HORIZONTAL STROKE					
一 一						

shù	VERTICAL STROKE					
｜ ↓						

piě	LEFT-FALLING STROKE					
ノ ノ						

nà	RIGHT-FALLING STROKE					
乀 乀						

diǎn	DOT					
丶 丶						

zhé	TURNING STROKE					
㇆ ㇆						

gōu	HOOK					
亅 亅						

tí	RISING STROKE					
ノ ノ						

héngzhéwāngōu						
乙 乙						

héngzhézhéwāngōu						
弓 弓						

数字　Numbers

yī	one							
一	一							

èr	two							
二	一	二						

sān	three							
三	一	二	三					

sì	four							
四	丨	冂	团	四	四			

wǔ	five / sound part							
五	一	丆	五	五				

liù	six							
六	丶	亠	六	六				

qī	seven / sound part							
七	一	七						

bā	eight / sound part							
八	丿	八						

jiǔ	nine / sound part							
九	丿	九						

shí	ten / sound part							
十	一	十						

位置形状　Position, Size & Amount

shàng	up; to go up, to go ahead / sound part							
上	丨	卜	上					

xià	down; to go down, to fall / sound part							
下	一	丁	下					

zhōng	middle, in / sound part							
中	丶	冂	口	中				

dà	big / sound part							
大	一	𠂇	大					

xiǎo	small, little / sound part							
小	亅	小	小					

shǎo	little, few	shào	young / sound part					
少	丨	丄	小	少				

duō	many, much / sound part							
多	丶	𠂊	夕	多				

bù	no, not / sound part							
不	一	丆	不	不				

人体　People

rén	person, people, man / sound part						
人	丿	人					

dānrénpáng	human - related radical (written on the left part)						
亻	丿	亻					

nǐ	you						
你	亻	伫	伫	伫	你		

nǚ	woman, female, daughter						
女	乚	夕	女				

mǔ	mother, female elder / sound part						
母	乚	口	毋	母	母		

fù	father, male relative of an elder generation / sound part						
父	丶	八	少	父			

lǎo	old; prefix / sound part						
老	一	十	土	耂	耂	老	

le	[used to show the completion of an action or a change of state] / sound part						
了	フ	了					

zǐ	son, child　zi　suffix / sound part						
子	フ	了	子				

ér	child, son　·r　suffix						
儿	丿	儿					

shēn	body						
身	′	′	丫	自	自	身	身

lì	to stand / sound part						
立	′	二	二	立	立		

cháng	long	zhǎng	to grow; leader, director / sound part				
长	′	二	长	长			

gè	[measure word]						
个	′	人	个				

lái	to come						
来	一	一	二	平	平	来	来

qù	to go, to leave / sound part						
去	一	十	土	去	去		

yìng'ěrduo(jié)	knee-related radical / sound part						
卩	丁	卩					

què	but						
却	却	却					

wǒ	I, me / sound part						
我	′	二	于	手	我	我	我

器官 Parts of the Body

tóu	head, beginning, top, end tou suffix						
头	`	⸍	三	头	头		

kǒu	mouth						
口	∣	冂	口				

mù	eye, item						
目	∣	冂	月	月	目		

zì	self, oneself; from						
自	⸍	亻	自	自	自	自	

ěr	ear / sound part						
耳	一	丆	丌	开	耳	耳	

miàn	face, surface, side, noodles						
面	一	丆	厂	而	而	而	面

jiàn	to look, to see / sound part						
见	∣	冂	贝	见			

yá	tooth / sound part						
牙	一	二	于	牙			

xīn	heart						
心	⸍	心	心	心			

yě	also, too						
也	刁	力	也				

shǒu	hand

手　ノ　二　三　手

tíshǒupáng(shǒu)	hand-related radical

扌　ノ　丁　扌

lā	to pull

拉　丁　扌　拉

fǎnwénpáng(pū)	hand-related radical

夂　ノ　㇇　夂　夂

jiāo	to teach

教　土　耂　教

zhǐ	to stop / sound part

止　｜　卜　卜　止

zú	foot; full, enough / sound part

足　丶　口　口　甲　甲　足　足

zúzìpáng	foot-related radical

𧾷　甲　𧾷

pā	to lie (on one's stomach), to bend over

趴　甲　足　趴　趴

zǒu	to walk, to go, to leave, to run

走　一　十　土　圥　走　走　走

bù		step					
步	⼁	⼘	⼞	止	歨	歨	步

zǒuzhīdǐ(chuò)		walking - or road - related radical					
辶	丶	辶	辶				

huán		to go or come back, to return	hái	still, yet			
还	不	还	还				

kě		can; but / sound part					
可	一	丆	丆	叮	可		

tiān	sky, day / sound part						
天	一	二	チ	天			

rì	sun, day						
日	丨	冂	日	日			

yuè	moon, month / sound part						
月	丿	刀	月	月			

xī	evening, sunset / sound part						
夕	丿	勹	夕				

yún	cloud / sound part						
云	一	二	云	云			

qì	air, gas						
气	丿	亇	气	气			

fēng	wind / sound part						
风	丿	几	凡	风			

yǔ	rain / sound part						
雨	一	一	冂	帀	帀	雨	雨

yǔzìtóu	weather-related radical						
雪	一	二	干	雪			

xuě	snow						
雪	雪	雪	雪				

diàn	electricity, lightning						
电	丶	冂	曰	日	电		

huǒ	fire / sound part						
火	丶	丷	少	火			

sìdiǎndǐ(huǒ)	fire-related radical						
灬	丿	八	灬	灬			

zhǔ	to cook, to boil						
煮	一	十	土	耂	耂	者	煮

guāng	light; bright; with nothing left; only / sound part						
光	丨	丷	少	业	光	光	

shuǐ		river, water						
水	亅	刁	水	水				

sāndiǎnshuǐ(shuǐ)		river- or water-related radical						
氵	丶	冫	氵					

hé		river						
河	冫	氵	河					

liǎngdiǎnshuǐ(bīng)		ice- or cold-related radical						
冫	丶	冫						

bīng		ice						
冰	丶	冫	冫	冰				

yǒng		forever, always / sound part						
永	丶	刁	永	永	永			

shān		mountain / sound part						
山	丨	山	山					

chū		to go or come out / sound part						
出	凵	凵	屮	出	出			

shí		stone, rock						
石	一	丁	丆	石	石			

tǔ		soil, land, dust / sound part						
土	一	十	土					

地理　Earth

zài	(to be) in, at, on						
在	一	大	大	右	在	在	

tián	field / sound part						
田	丨	冂	日	田	田		

lǐ	inner, inside; lane, neighborhood; Chinese mile (equal to 500 meters) / sound part						
里	丨	冂	日	日	甲	甲	里

zuǒ'ěrpáng(fù)	mountain- or area-related radical						
阝	乛	阝					

yáng	the sun, sunlight						
阳	乛	阝	阝	阳			

niú	cattle				
牛	ノ	⌐	乞	牛	

yáng	sheep, goat / sound part				
羊	ヽ	ヾ	丷	丷	兰 羊

mǎ	horse / sound part			
马	フ	马	马	

lóng	dragon / sound part			
龙	一	十	尤	龙 龙

hǔ	tiger / sound part					
虎	✝	⊢	上	卢	卢	卢 虎

tù	rabbit					
兔	ノ	勹	𠂉	臽	兔	兔 兔

xiàng	elephant / sound part				
象	鱼	争	豸	象	象 象

quǎn	dog			
犬	一	十	大	犬

动物 Animals

niǎo	bird / sound part						
鸟	✓	勹	勺	鸟	鸟		

chóng	insect, worm / sound part						
虫	丶	冂	口	中	虫	虫	

fǎnquǎnpáng (quǎn)	animal-related radical						
犭	✓	犭	犭				

dú	single, alone						
独	犭	犭	独				

yú	fish						
鱼	✓	夕	仈	鱼	角	鱼	鱼

jiǎo	horn, angle, corner; [a unit of Chinese currency] / sound part						
角	勹	勽	角	角	角		

máo	feather, hair, fur; [equivalent to "角" in spoken Chinese] / sound part						
毛	✓	二	三	毛			

ròu	meat						
肉	冂	内	内	肉	肉		

xiě, xuè	blood						
血	✓	亻	冖	血	血	血	

xí	to practice						
习	习	习	习				

fēi	to fly							
飞	㇠	飞	飞					

zhuī	short-tailed bird (in classical Chinese); bird-related radical / sound part							
佳	亻	亻	亻	佇	佳	佳		

tuī	to push							
推	扌	推						

chéng	to become, to succeed / sound part							
成	一	厂	厈	成	成	成		

植物 Plants

mù	wood, tree / sound part						
木	一	十	才	木			

guǒ	fruit, result / sound part						
果	冂	冂	日	旦	早	果	果

shū	foot-related radical / sound part						
疋	乛	丁	牙	疋			

chǔ	clear, grieved						
楚	一	十	林	梺	棥	梺	楚

shēng	to give birth to, to grow; rare (for meat), not ripe (for fruit); student / sound part						
生	丿	丿	𠂉	牛	生		

zhú	bamboo						
竹	丿	𠂉	竹	𥫗	𥫗	竹	

zhúzìtóu	bamboo-related radical / sound part						
𥫗	丿	𠂉	𥫗				

bǐ	Chinese brush pen, pen						
笔	𠂉	𥫗	竹	竺	筌	笔	

hé	cereal seedlings, standing grain / sound part						
禾	丿	二	千	禾	禾		

nián	year, age						
年	丿	𠂉	𠂉	乍	年		

植物　Plants

mǐ	rice; meter (for measurement) / sound part					
米	丶	丷	丷	半	米	米

duǒ	[measure word for flowers, clouds] / sound part					
朵	丿	几	几	朵	朵	朵

guā	melon / sound part					
瓜	乀	厂	瓜	瓜	瓜	

cǎozìtóu	grass- or plant-related radical					
艹	一	十	艹			

cǎo	grass					
草	一	艹	艹	节	苩	苴	草

yòu'érpáng(yì)		city - or place - related radical				
阝	𠃌	阝				

dū	city	dōu	all			
都	耂	者	者阝	都		

chǎng	factory					
厂	一	厂				

guǎng	wide / sound part					
广	丶	亠	广			

gāo	high, tall / sound part					
高	丶	亠	亠	𠌫	高	高	高

shùxīnpáng(xīn)		heart - related radical				
忄	丶	丷	忄			

jīng	to startle, to be frightened					
惊	忄	忄	忄	怜	惊	惊

mén	door / sound part					
门	丶	门	门			

xiàng	direction; toward / sound part					
向	丿	亻	门	向	向	

hù	door, family / sound part					
户	丶	亠	㇆	户		

建筑 Buildings

bǎogàitóu(mián)　house- related radical

宀　丶　宀　宀

jiā　home, family

家　宀　宁　宁　宇　家　家　家

xíng　to walk, to go, to do; OK　háng　trade

行　丿　彳　彳　彳　行　行

shuāngrénpáng(chí)　walking-related radical

彳　彳

hěn　very

很　彳　彳　彳　很　很

wǎ　tile on the roof

瓦　一　瓦　瓦　瓦

yǐ　as / sound part

以　丶　以　以　以

liǎng　two / sound part

两　一　一　丙　丙　两　两

jīn	half a kilogram / sound part						
斤	丶	厂	厂	斤			

bīng	soldier, weapon / sound part						
兵	厂	厂	斤	丘	兵	兵	

gōng	bow / sound part						
弓	ㄱ	ㄱ	弓				

wán	pellet, pill						
丸	丿	九	丸				

yòng	to use / sound part						
用	丿	冂	月	月	用		

me	suffix						
么	丶	幺	么				

gōng	work / sound part						
工	一	丅	工				

dāo	knife / sound part						
刀	𠃌	刀					

lì	strength, force, power / sound part						
力	𠃌	力					

wǎng	net						
网	冂	冈	冈	网	网		

sìzìtóu(sì, wǎng)	net- or guilt-relatad radical						
罒	冂	罒	罒				

luó	net for catching birds						
罗	罒	罗	罗				

chē	car, vehicle						
车	一	𠂉	𠂆	车			

zhōu	boat						
舟	丶	丿	月	月	舟	舟	

yī	clothes / sound part						
衣	亠	亠	亠	衣	衣		

guǒ	to wrap						
裹	東	東	裏	裏	裹		

yīzìpáng(yī)	clothes-related radical						
衤	㇇	衤	衤	衤			

chū	beginning						
初	衤	初					

jīn	a piece of cloth						
巾	丨	冂	巾				

dài	belt; to bring with, to carry						
带	一	卄	卅	卅	芇	带	带

bèi	shell / sound part						
贝	丨	冂	贝	贝			

jīn	gold, metal, money						
金	丿	人	仝	仐	仝	全	金

jīnzìpáng(jīn)	metal-related radical / sound part						
钅	亅	𠂆	钅	钅			

zhōng	bell, clock						
钟	钅	钟					

wáng　　king / sound part

王　二　干　王

yù　　jade

玉　干　王　玉

器具 Household Objects

jī	small table	jǐ	several; how many, what / sound part			
几	丿	几				

píng	equal, calm, flat / sound part					
平	一	一	亓	亚	平	

jīn	now, today / sound part					
今	丿	人	仌	今		

huì	to meet; meeting; can / sound part					
会	人	仌	会			

hé	to shut or close, to fit / sound part					
合	人	仌	合			

gǒng	hand-related radical					
廾	一	十	廾			

kāi	to open, to turn on					
开	二	开	开			

cè	volume

| 册 | 丿 | 刀 | 刑 | 刑 | 册 | | |

diǎn	law, standard, ceremony / sound part

| 典 | 冂 | 冂 | 由 | 曲 | 曲 | 典 | 典 |

wén	character, writing, culture / sound part

| 文 | 丶 | 亠 | 宀 | 文 | | | |

bái	white, clear, pure / sound part

| 白 | 丿 | 亻 | 白 | 白 | 白 | | |

hēi	black, dark, shady

| 黑 | 冂 | 四 | 四 | 甲 | 里 | 罪 | 黑 |

yè	course of study, trade

| 业 | 丨 | 刂 | 刂l | 业 | 业 | | |

zhà	at first, suddenly / sound part

| 乍 | 乀 | 亻 | 午 | 乍 | | | |

zuò	to do, to work

| 作 | 亻 | 作 | | | | | |

lìdāopáng(dāo)	knife-related radical

| 刂 | 丨 | 刂 | | | | | |

bié	other; don't

| 别 | 号 | 另 | 另 | 别 | | | |

人体　People

shī	dead body							
尸	フ	コ	尸					

bāozìtóu	wrap-related radical							
勹	ノ	勹						

bāo	to wrap; bag, package / sound part							
包	勹	勹	勹	包				

jiāo	to cross, to associate with, to hand over / sound part							
交	丶	一	六	六	亣	交		

dòu	to fight	dǒu	[a unit of dry measure for grain] / sound part					
斗	丶	丷	三	斗				

jiǔ	long time / sound part							
久	ノ	勹	久					

bǐ	to compare, to compete / sound part							
比	一	匕	比	比				

bìng	to combine; and / sound part							
并	丶	丷	丷	兰	羊	并		

mín	people / sound part							
民	フ	コ	尸	尸	民			

gèng	more, even more / sound part							
更	一	一	丆	百	百	更	更	

fā	to shoot, to begin	fà	hair / sound part				
发	㇀	㇀𠂇	𠂇㇇	𠂇㇇㇏	发		

shǒu	head; first						
首	丶	丷	丷	艹	𦣞	首	首

shé	tongue						
舌	丿	二	千	千	舌	舌	

yán	speech, word						
言	丶	一	二	三	言	言	言

yánzìpáng（yán）	speech-related radical						
讠	丶	讠	讠				

huà	talk; word						
话	讠	讠	讠	话			

yīn	sound, voice						
音	丶	亠	立	产	音	音	

qiàn	to yawn, to lack, to owe / sound part						
欠	丿	𠂉	勹	欠			

dǎi	bad, evil						
歹	一	一	歹	歹			

shì	person, soldier						
士	一	十	士				

zhuǎ，zhǎo	claw						
爪	丿	厂	爪	爪			

zhǎozìtóu(zhuǎ)　　hand-related radical

爫　　丶　　⺈　　⺈　　⺈

cǎi　　to pick, to gather

采　　⺈　　⺈　　采

yòu　　again

又　　フ　　又

qiú　　to beg, to ask for, to seek / sound part

求　　一　　丁　　寸　　扌　　氺　　求

shū　　hand-related radical

殳　　几　　⺈　　殳

tóu　　to throw

投　　扌　　护　　投

fǎn　　opposite / sound part

反　　一　　厂　　厅　　反

wú　　naught, nothing / sound part

无　　一　　二　　无　　无

xiān　　before, firstly / sound part

先　　丿　　⺊　　牛　　生　　牛　　先

gǔ	valley; grain / sound part						
谷	丶	八	八	父	谷	谷	谷

chuān	river, plain / sound part						
川	丿	刂	川				

zhōu	state, land, district						
州	丶	丿	少	州	州	州	

bā	to be close to, to long for; suffix / sound part						
巴	乛	刀	刃	刃	巴		

lì	beautiful						
丽	一	一	丁	月	月	丽	

pí	leather, skin; naughty / sound part						
皮	乛	厂	广	皮	皮		

gé	leather; to change, to expel						
革	一	十	廿	甘	芇	苗	革

gǔ	bone / sound part						
骨	丶	冂	冎	冎	骨	骨	骨

fēi	wrong; not / sound part						
非	丨	刂	非	非	非	非	

nóng	agriculture, farm / sound part						
农	丶	冖	宀	农	农	农	

dōng	东	east / sound part
xī	西	west / sound part
zhǐ	夂	foot-related radical
gè	各	each, every / sound part

植物　Plants

cái	just; ability / sound part							
才	一	十	才					

fēng	plentiful / sound part							
丰	一	二	三	丰				

shù	bundle; to tie, to bind / sound part							
束	一	丆	亇	亜	束	束	束	

shí	food; to eat							
食	人	入	今	今	今	食	食	

shízìpáng (shí)	food-related radical							
饣	丿	𠂊	饣					

fàn	cooked rice, meal							
饭	𠂊	饣	饭					

shì	family name / sound part							
氏	丿	𠂆	氏	氏				

dǐ	base / sound part							
氐	氐	氐						

wǔ	noon							
午	丿	𠂉	午	午				

hòu	after, back, behind / sound part							
后	一	厂	厂	斤	后	后		

植物　Plants

tóng	same / sound part						
同	丨	冂	冂	同	同	同	

qián	former, first, front / sound part						
前	丷	丷	竹	竹	首	前	前

xué	hole, cave, nest					
穴	丶	八	宀	宂	穴	

cōng	chimney					
囱	丿	内	囱			

chuāng	window					
窗	宀	宂	窗	窗	窗	

tūbǎogài(mì)	cover-related radical					
冖	丶	冖				

jūn	army					
军	丶	冖	写	军		

cāng	storehouse, warehouse / sound part					
仓	丿	人	仐	仓		

shè	house	shě	to give up / sound part			
舍	人	人	仒	仝	仝	舍 舍

jǐng	well / sound part					
井	一	二	丰	井		

máo	lance / sound part					
矛	乛	矛	马	予	矛	

dùn	shield / sound part					
盾	一	厂	厂	厈	厉	盾

gān		to interfere; dry	gàn		to do / sound part			
干	一	二	干					

gē		dagger-ax (ancient Chinese weapon)						
戈	一	弋	戈	戈				

zuǒ		hand-related radical						
ナ	一	ナ						

yǒu		friend						
友	一	ナ	方	友				

建筑·武器　Buildings & Weapons

xìng	favor; lucky						
幸	+	士	士	去	去	幸	幸

xīn	laborious, sad, spicy / sound part						
辛	丶	亠	六	立	立	辛	

fāng	direction, side; method; square / sound part			
方	丶	亠	方	方

hù	each other			
互	一	乛	互	互

xì	system, series, department	jì	to tie			
系	一	乛	玄	玄	系	系	系

jiǎosīpáng（mì，sī）	textile-related radical	
纟	乡	纟

hóng	red		
红	纟	纟	红

yǔ	to give; and; with / sound part	
与	一	与

biǎo	surface; watch / sound part					
表	二	丰	丰	夫	表	表	表

qū	to bend	qǔ	music				
曲	丨	冂	冂	由	曲	曲	

shēng	to rise; liter						
升	ノ	二	千	升			

zuǒfāngkuāng(fāng)		box-related radical					
匚	一	匚					

qū	district; to distinguish						
区	一	丆	又	区			

jù	huge / sound part						
巨	一	丐	王	巨			

shū	book, letter; to write						
书	乛	乛	书	书			

sè	color						
色	ノ	夕	夕	各	多	色	

yè	page						
页	一	丆	丆	百	页	页	

yuè	music	lè	happy / sound part				
乐	ノ	二	千	牙	乐		

sǐ	to die						
死	一	丆	歹	歹	歹	死	

rù	to enter, to join						
入	丿	入					

nèi	inside / sound part						
内	丨	冂	内	内			

xí	banquet, seat / sound part						
席	丶	广	广	庐	庐	庐	席

piàn	slice, thin piece; [measure word for land, field, etc.]						
片	丿	丿	片	片			

qí	neat; together / sound part						
齐	丶	二	亠	文	文	齐	

zhōu	all; circumference, week / sound part						
周	冂	刀	用	用	用	周	周

wáng	to escape, to flee, to die / sound part						
亡	丶	亠	亡				

zhǔ	main / sound part						
主	丶	二	主	主			

shēng	sound						
声	一	十	士	吉	吉	声	声

wù	don't / sound part						
勿	丿	勹	勿	勿			

cùn	*cun* (a Chinese unit of length equal to 3.33 centimeters); very little / sound part					
寸	一	寸	寸			

zhàng	*zhang* (a Chinese unit of length equal to 3. 33 meters); husband / sound part					
丈	一	ナ	丈			

bǎi	hundred; all kinds of / sound part					
百	一	一	丆	苪	百	百

qiān	thousand, a great number / sound part					
千	丿	二	千			

wàn	ten thousand, a very great number					
万	一	丁	万			

dān	single, odd / sound part					
单	丶	丷	씸	씸	㘴	单

bàn	half; in the middle / sound part					
半	丶	丷	丷	半	半	

xìng	excitement, interest		xīng	to prevail, to rise, to start		
兴	丶	丷	丷	兴	兴	兴

其他　Others

shāng	trade; to discuss						
商	亠	亠	亠	产	商	商	商

yuán	person engaged in some field of activity / sound part						
员	口	口	尸	吊	员	员	

zhì	to, until / sound part						
至	一	云	云	丢	至	至	

lìng	to order, to let / sound part						
令	丿	人	仒	今	令		

chéng	to bear, to undertake						
承	了	了	孑	承	承	承	

shī	to lose / sound part						
失	丿	仁	乍	牛	失		

shǐ	arrow						
矢	仁	仁	午	矢			

yī	doctor, medicine						
医	一	区	医				

yǐ	second / sound part						
乙	乙						

bìngzìtóu(nè)	sickness-related radical						
疒	丶	广	疒	疒			

bìng	ill, sick						
病	疒	病	病				

dīng	fourth / sound part						
丁	一	丁					

nán	south						
南	十	十	南	南	南	南	南

běi	north / sound part						
北	丨	丬	扌	北			

dì	younger brother / sound part						
弟	丶	丷	丷	兰	弟	弟	

gē	elder brother / sound part						
哥	一	可	可	可	哥		

jí	and; to reach, to be equal to / sound part						
及	丿	乃	及				

yǐ	already						
已	𠃌	コ	已				

jǐ	oneself / sound part						
己	𠃌	コ	己				

ér	and, but						
而	一	丆	丆	而	而	而	

zài	again
再	一　一丁　一丁　丙　丙　再

jiǎ	first; shell / sound
甲	冂　曰　甲

yóu	cause / sound part
由	冂　甶　由

yú	than, for, to, at / sound part
于	一　二　于

chǎn	to produce / sound part
产	丶　亠　亠　六　立　产

xiāng	countryside
乡	ㄥ　�　乡

yóu	especially / sound part
尤	一　ナ　尤　尤

zhī	of; it, him, her
之	丶　㇇　之

hū	[question word] / sound part
乎	一　丷　爫　乊　乎

zhě	person; (old use) this / sound part
者	一　十　土　耂　耂　者

其他　Others

jiànzìdǐ(yǐn)　walk-related radical

廴　廴　廴

jiàn　to build

建　⺲　⺲　⺲　建

bǔ　fortune-telling / sound part

卜　丨　卜

chù　place, section　　**chǔ**　to get along with sb., to be situated in

处　丿　夂　夂　处

jiù　old, past, used

旧　丨　刂　刂　旧　旧

zhuān　to monopolize, to focus on sth. / sound part

专　一　二　专　专

sī　private / sound part

厶　厶　厶

gōng　public, male

公　丿　八　公　公

wéi　to do, to act as　　**wèi**　for

为　丶　丷　为　为

bàn　to do, to handle

办　フ　力　办　办

其他 Others

wèi — to guard, to defend, to protect						
卫	乛	卫	卫			
bì — must, have to / sound part						
必	丶	心	心	必	必	
shǐ — history / sound part						
史	冂	口	史	史		
dāng — when; to be as / sound part dàng — proper						
当	⌐	⼎	凵	当	当	当
guān — to close						
关	丷	丷	丷	䒑	关	关
qiě — even; just / sound part						
且	丨	冂	目	目	且	
xiàn — county / sound part						
县	丨	冂	目	目	且	县
qí — such, its / sound part						
其	一	廿	廿	苴	其	其
zhí — straight / sound part						
直	十	十	古	古	直	
zhēn — indeed, really / sound part						
真	十	十	古	古	直	真	真

jù	utensil, tool; to possess, to have / sound part						
具	冂	冂	且	具	具		

gèn	solid, hard / sound part						
艮	ㄱ	ㅋ	㠯	艮			

liáng	fine / sound part						
良	丶	白	良				

chén	time / sound part						
辰	厂	厂	厇	辰	辰	辰	

lín	to arrive, to face; just before						
临	㇀	忄	忄	临	临	临	临

jǔ	to lift , to hold						
举	丶	丷	兴	兴	兴	兴	举

gòng	altogether; common / sound part						
共	一	十	卄	共	共	共	

jì	already / sound part						
既	ㄱ	艮	艮	既	既	既	既

páng	side; beside; other / sound part						
旁	丶	亠	立	产	产	旁	旁

yú	to remain / sound part						
余	人	全	全	全	全	余	

其他　Others

yòu	(variant of "又")　hand-related radical						
⺕	フ	⺕	⺕				

zhēng	to contend, to argue / sound part						
争	⺈	⺈	争				

qīng	green, young, dark blue / sound part						
青	二	丰	圭	丰	青	青	青

huáng	yellow / sound part						
黄	十	卄	艹	芏	昔	苗	黄

jiè	to lie between, to introduce briefly / sound part						
介	ノ	人	介	介			

lí	away, to leave / sound part					
离	亠	文	云	卤	离	离

yú	a kind of monkey (in classical Chinese) / sound part					
禺	口	日	月	禺		

yù	to meet					
遇	口	日	月	禺	㝢	遇

shì	to show, to notify, to instruct					
示	一	二	于	亍	示	

shìzìpáng(shì)	religion-related radical / sound part					
礻	丶	㇇	礻	礻		

shén	deity					
神	礻	祊	神			

guǐ	ghost / sound part					
鬼	丿	白	甶	兜	鬼	鬼

yì	justice, significance; equitable / sound part					
义	丶	丷	义			

lán	orchid / sound part					
兰	丶	丷	丷	半	兰	

yán	tight, strict					
严	一	丆	严	亚	亚	亚	严

chǒu	ugly, disgraceful / sound part						
丑	刁	刁	丑	丑			

biǎn	flat / sound part						
扁	⺁	户	户	启	扁	扁	

yì	also, too / sound part						
亦	丶	亠	亣	亦	亦		

wéi	(written language) leather / sound part						
韦	一	二	彐	韦			

dòu	bean / sound part						
豆	一	一	口	豆	豆		

bō	foot-related radical						
癶	丁	夕	癶	癶			

dēng	to ascend, to step on, to publish						
登	癶	癶	咎	登			

fǒu	(old use) earthern ware; pot-related radical						
缶	人	午	缶				

quē	to be short of, to lack; incomplete						
缺	生	缶	缸	缺			

jiū	sound part						
丩	𡿨	丩					

shōu	to receive						
收	丩	丩'	收	收			

yǒu	ferment-related radical						
酉	丆	襾	襾	酉			

jiǔ	wine						
酒	氵	酒					

mǐn	household utensils; utensil-related radical						
皿	冂	冂	皿	皿			

hé	box						
盒	合	侖	盒				

sānpiěr (shān)	color- or shape-related radical / sound part						
彡	丿	彡	彡				

cǎi	colorful						
彩	采	彩	彩				

yāng	center / sound part						
央	冂	叹	叹	央			

yīng	hero, England						
英	一	艹	苎	英			

guāi	sound part						
夬	乛	ユ	夬	夬			

kuài	quick, happy							
快	忄	忄	快					

áng	sound part							
印	ノ	⺈	白	印				

yíng	to welcome, to meet							
迎	卬	迎						

hài	sound part							
亥	亠	云	亥	亥				

hái	child							
孩	孑	孖	孩	孩				

qiāng	sound part							
丬	丶	丬						

jiāng	shall, would / sound part							
将	丶	丬	㸪	㸪	将			

jiù	mortar / sound part							
臼	丿	千	臼	臼	臼			

jiù	mother's brother							
舅	臼	臽	畠	舅				

yāo	youngest; little-related radical							
幺	乡	幺	幺					

yòu	young, underage						
幼	幺	幻	幼				

nǎi	to be; so / sound part						
乃	乃	乃					

nǎi	milk, breast						
奶	乚	女	奶	奶			

gān	sweet, pleasant / sound part						
甘	一	廿	甘	甘			

tián	sweet						
甜	丿	舌	舌	甜			

sī	to manage / sound part						
司	ㄱ	ㄢ	司	司			

cí	word						
词	讠	订	词	词			

quàn	sound part						
关	丷	丷	半	关			

quán	fist						
拳	丷	半	关	拳			

yǒng	corridor / sound part						
甬	乛	乛	乛	甬			

tòng	pain						
痛	疒	疒	痏	痛			

fǔ	(written language) just, only / sound part						
甫	一	甬	甫	甫			

fǔ	to assist						
辅	车	斩	辅	辅			

jiǎn	sound part						
东	亡	专	东	东			

liàn	to smelt						
炼	丶	灯	炼	炼			

jìng	(written language) network (of rivers, streams, etc.) / sound part						
圣	又	圣	圣	圣			

jīng	to manage; constant						
经	纟	纟	经				

yáng	sound part						
昜	马	马	昜				

tāng	soup						
汤	丶	氵	汤	汤			

fú	not / sound part						
弗	弓	弓	弗	弗			

fó	Buddha					
佛	亻	亻	佛	佛		

yǔ	to give / sound part					
予	乛	マ	�301	予		

yù	in advance, beforehand					
预	予	予	预			

shàng	still, yet / sound part					
尚	丷	丷	屮	尚	尚	

cháng	often					
常	丷	丷	尚	常		

jué	to feel, to wake (up)					
觉	丶	丷	丷	兴	觉	

xué	to learn					
学	丶	丷	学	学		